Spelling

Key Stage 1
For ages 5-7

Practise & Learn

Published by CGP

Editors:
Claire Boulter
Holly Poynton
Rebecca Tate

With thanks to Luke Antieul and
Kim Sissons for the proofreading.

ISBN: 978 1 84762 742 1
www.cgpbooks.co.uk
Printed by Elanders Ltd, Newcastle upon Tyne
Clipart from Corel®

Contents

Spelling simple words

Words are made up of different sounds.

Say these sounds out loud.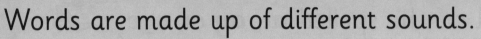

Put the sounds together to spell the word. ⟹ rat

Changing one sound in a word makes a new word.
Change a sound in each word so it matches the picture.

run 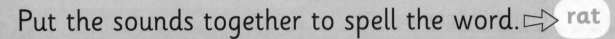 sun .... pin ....

far .... not ....

big .... tip ....

Write eight words using any three letters on the frog.

.... sit ....

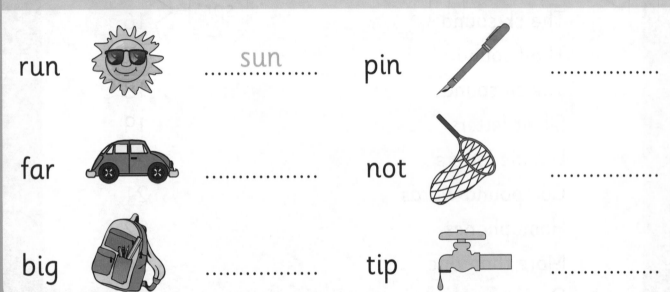

....

....

....

4

The ai sound

The **ai** sound can be spelled **ai**, **ay** or **a_e**.

Say these words out loud. ➡ n**ai**l   d**ay**   g**a**m**e**

Write **ai** or **ay** to finish each word.

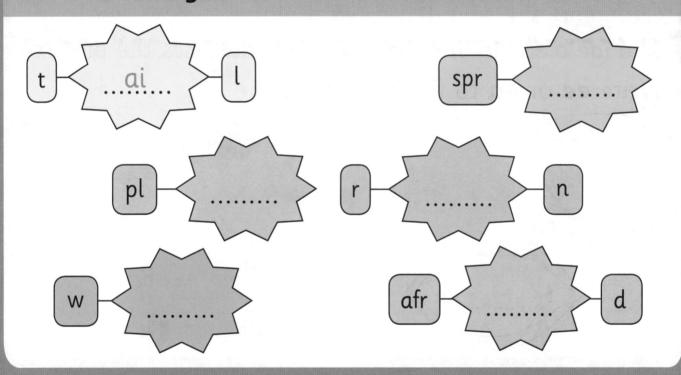

t — ...ai... — l

spr — ....

pl — ....

r — .... — n

w — ....

afr — .... — d

Write the right spelling of each word.

stane   cayk   trai   snayl

stain   ....

spaid   aym   graipe   playt

....

5

ee and ie sounds

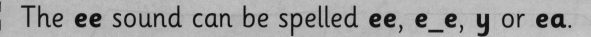

The **ee** sound can be spelled **ee**, **e_e**, **y** or **ea**.

Say these words out loud. ⇨ see these happy pea

The **ie** sound can be spelled **ie**, **y**, **i_e** or **igh**.

Say these words out loud. ⇨ pie fly like sigh

Write **ee** or **ea** to finish each word.

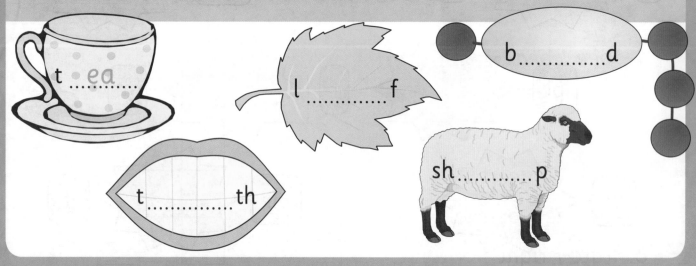

t......ea......

l...............f

b..............d

t...............th

sh..............p

Write the right spelling of each word on the pad.

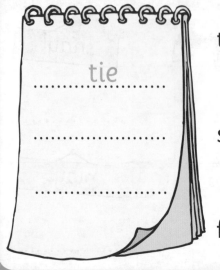

tie

....

....

tigh / tie

skie / sky

flight / flyt

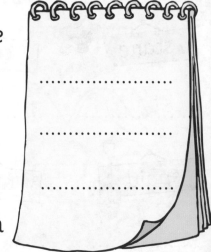

....

....

byke / bike

light / lite

why / wigh

6

Write three words with the **ee** sound on the sweet.
Write three words with the **ie** sound on the kite.

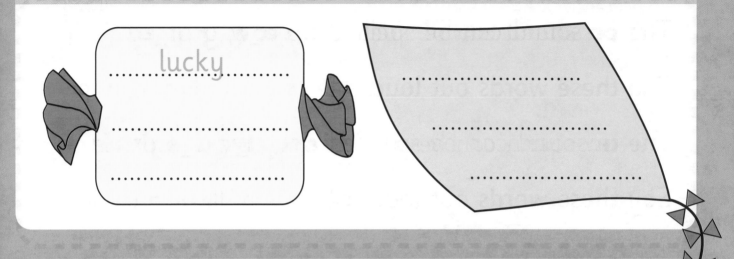

..........lucky..........

....

....

....

....

....

Choose the right spelling to fill in the word puzzle.

1. bee / bea
2. teech / teach
3. crie / cry
4. yeast / yeest
5. breaze / breeze
6. ryte / right
7. high / hy
8. eies / eyes
9. unty / untie

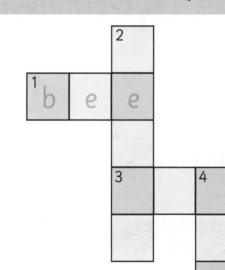

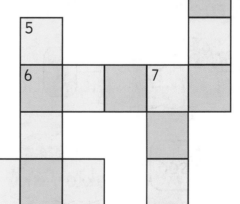

oa and oo sounds

The **oa** sound can be spelled **oa**, **ow** or **o_e**.

Say these words out loud. ⇨ coat   low   rope

The **oo** sound can be spelled **oo**, **ew**, **u_e** or **ue**.

Say these words out loud. ⇨ soon flew rule glue

Colour in the words that are spelled right.

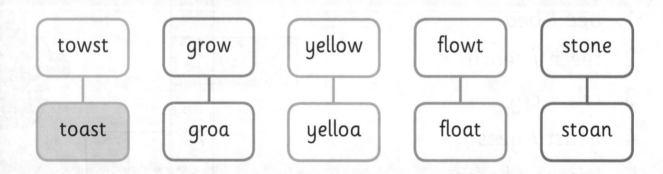

| towst | grow | yellow | flowt | stone |
| toast | groa | yelloa | float | stoan |

Write **oo**, **ew** or **ue** in each jelly to make a word.

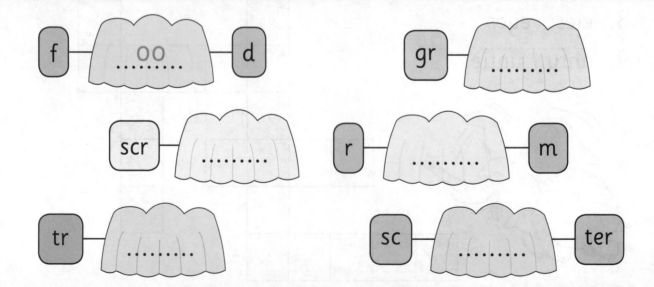

f — oo......... — d   gr — ....

scr — ....   r — .... — m

tr — ....   sc — .... — ter

Write the letters in the right order to spell the word.

blew

....

Cross out one letter from each word so it is spelled right. Write the letter you crossed out in the box to show the secret message.

| coipe | throaw | soask | caretoon | jewell |

| cclue | phonne | soapp | argule |

| i | | | | | | | | |

Use the letters in the book to write six words with the oa or oo sound on the board.

note

....

....

....

9

oi and ow sounds

The **oi** sound can be spelled **oi** or **oy**.

Say these words out loud. ⇨ | **oi**l   **joy**

The **ow** sound can be spelled **ow** or **ou**.

Say these words out loud. ⇨ | t**ow**el   m**ou**se

Write the letters in the right order to spell the **oi** word.

..........soil.................   ....

Draw a ring around the right spelling of each word.

(toy) / toi

coyn / coin

point / poynt

royal / roil

boi / boy

voyce / voice

Write **ow** or **ou** in each train to make a word.

cl ...ou... d   t .... er   cr .... n

gr .... nd   gr l   s .... nd

Write a word with the **ow** sound to match each picture.

brown ....

....

Find the words with the **ow** and **oi** sounds.

loud
frown
pound
how
count

l	o	u	d	x	r	t	a	l	h	o
z	y	i	e	o	a	d	n	u	o	w
s	p	o	i	l	t	y	n	f	w	t
i	c	j	z	p	f	s	o	n	r	q
c	o	u	n	t	r	t	y	l	k	j
v	i	e	a	t	o	x	j	o	y	o
p	l	j	h	g	w	z	s	j	y	i
e	x	p	o	u	n	d	d	a	n	n

coil
spoil
annoy
join
joy

ur, ar and or sounds

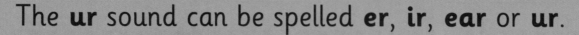

> The **ur** sound can be spelled **er**, **ir**, **ear** or **ur**.
>
> Say these words out loud. ⟹ her   dirt   **ear**n   n**ur**se
>
> The **ar** sound can be spelled **ar**, **a** or **al**.
>
> Say these words out loud. ⟹ jar   father   half

Write **er**, **ir** or **ur** to finish the words.

div er

p.......se

........th

tig........

th......d

sk.......t

Make six words with the **ar** sound using these letters.

.....palm......

....

....

....

....

....

The **or** sound can be spelled **or**, **au**, **oor**, **ore**, **al** or **aw**.

Say these words out loud! ➡ port haunt floor snore walk paw

Finish each word using the right spelling of the **or** sound.

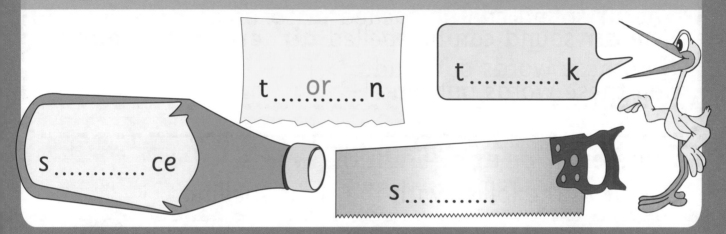

t......or......n

t.............k

s.............ce

s.............

Ring the **or** words that are spelled right.

It was a sunny **mauning** / (**morning**) in **August** / **Orgust**. Samia and Ben were sitting on the **lorn** / **lawn**. Ben was reading a **story** / **stawry** book and Samia was **drooring** / **drawing**. "I'm **bored** / **bawed**," said Ben, "let's do something **sporty** / **spawty**." Samia picked up a **ball** / **borl** and ran to the end of the garden. "Let's play catch," she **cawled** / **called**.

Write the right spelling of each **or** word.

 strau

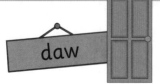 daw

 shawt

 taul

straw ....

ear and air sounds

The **ear** sound can be spelled **ere**, **ear** or **eer**.

Say these words out loud. 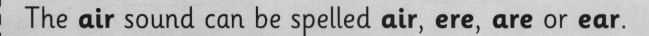 here   fear   steer

The **air** sound can be spelled **air**, **ere**, **are** or **ear**.

Say these words out loud. fair   there   dare   wear

Colour in the lollies with the right spelling.

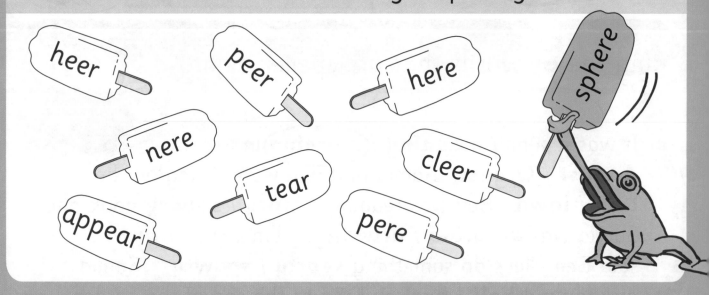

heer   peer   here   sphere

nere   tear   cleer

appear   pere

Use the letters to write six words with the **air** sound.

c   i
  e
s   n
  r
d   a
t   f   w

care ....

....

....

Colour in the words that are spelled right.

yeer	spair	gear	rare	severe
year	spare	gere	rair	seveer

Cross out one letter from each word so it is spelled right. Write the letter you crossed out in the box to show the secret message.

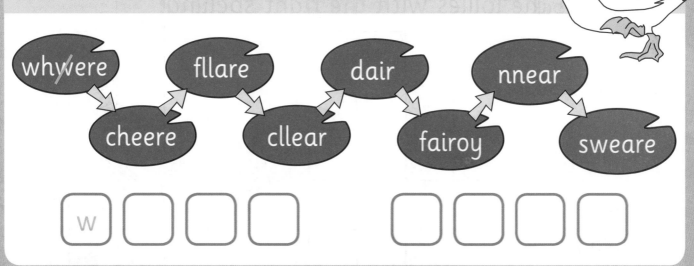

whwere → cheere → fllare → cllear → dair → fairoy → nnear → sweare

[w] [ ] [ ] [ ]   [ ] [ ] [ ] [ ]

Write the **air** or **ear** word for each picture.

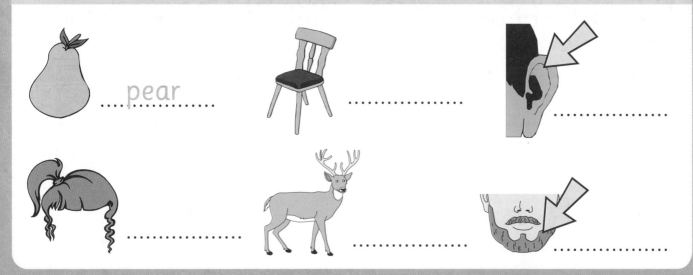

.....pear..... ....

....

15

The ck sound

Quack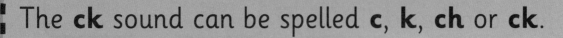

The **ck** sound can be spelled **c**, **k**, **ch** or **ck**.

Say these words out loud. ⇨ **c**at **k**ind **ch**emist blo**ck**

Choose the right spelling to fill the word puzzle.

1. school / skool
2. cloak / cloack
3. lok / lock
4. kot / cot
5. care / chare
6. kit / cit
7. tik / tick
8. parc / park
9. eko / echo
10. oac / oak

Write a word with the **ck** sound for each picture.

 clock

 ....

 ....

 ....

 ....

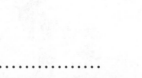 ....

Practise and Learn

Spelling
Ages 5-7

Answers

This section shows each of the pages from the book with the answers filled out.

The pages are laid out in the same way as the book itself, so the questions can be easily marked by you, or by your child.

There are also helpful learning tips with some of the pages.

4

Spelling simple words

Words are made up of different sounds.
Say these sounds out loud. ⇨ r a t
Put the sounds together to spell the word. ⇨ rat

Changing one sound in a word makes a new word.
Change a sound in each word so it matches the picture.

run	sun	pin	pen
far	car	not	net
big	bag	tip	tap

Write eight words using any three letters on the frog.

sit	son
nap	rip
pet	rat
not	pea

OTHER ANSWERS POSSIBLE
e a i

4

If your child finds the second exercise tricky, try writing the letters on scraps of paper that they can move around to make words.

5

The ai sound

The **ai** sound can be spelled **ai**, **ay** or **a_e**.
Say these words out loud. ⇨ nail   day   game

Write **ai** or **ay** to finish each word.

t ai l   spr ay
pl ay   r ai n
w ay   afr ai d

Write the right spelling of each word.

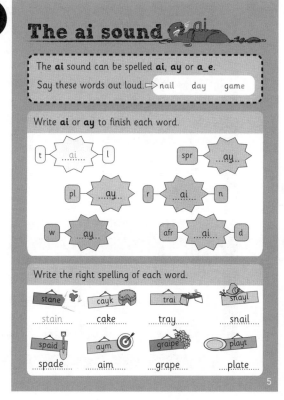

stane	cayk	trai	snayl
stain	cake	tray	snail
spaid	aym	graipe	playt
spade	aim	grape	plate

5

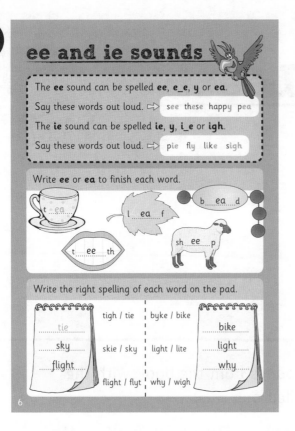

6 · ee and ie sounds

The **ee** sound can be spelled **ee**, **e_e**, **y** or **ea**.

Say these words out loud. ⇨ see these happy pea

The **ie** sound can be spelled **ie**, **y**, **i_e** or **igh**.

Say these words out loud. ⇨ pie fly like sigh

Write **ee** or **ea** to finish each word.

t _ea_
l _ea_ f
b _ea_ d
t _ee_ th
sh _ee_ p

Write the right spelling of each word on the pad.

tie	tigh / tie
sky	skie / sky
flight	flight / flyt

byke / bike	_bike_
light / lite	_light_
why / wigh	_why_

6

7

Write three words with the **ee** sound on the sweet.
Write three words with the **ie** sound on the kite.

lucky
VARIOUS ANSWERS POSSIBLE

Choose the right spelling to fill in the word puzzle.

1. bee / bea
2. teech / teach
3. crie / cry
4. yeast / yeest
5. breaze / breeze
6. ryte / right
7. high / hy
8. eies / eyes
9. unty / untie

Crossword answers:
1. b e e
2. t e a c h
3. c r y
4. y e a s t
5. b r e e z
6. r i g h t
7. h i g h
8. e y e s
9. u n t i e

7

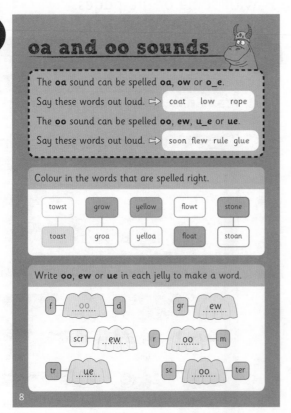

8 · oa and oo sounds

The **oa** sound can be spelled **oa**, **ow** or **o_e**.

Say these words out loud. ⇨ coat low rope

The **oo** sound can be spelled **oo**, **ew**, **u_e** or **ue**.

Say these words out loud. ⇨ soon flew rule glue

Colour in the words that are spelled right.

towst	grow	yellow	flowt	stone
toast	groa	yelloa	float	stoan

Write **oo**, **ew** or **ue** in each jelly to make a word.

f _oo_ d
gr _ew_
scr _ew_
r _oo_ m
tr _ue_
sc _oo_ ter

8

9

Write the letters in the right order to spell the word.

blew   _zoom_   _boat_

Cross out one letter from each word so it is spelled right. Write the letter you crossed out in the box to show the secret message.

coipe   throgw   soask   caretoon   jewelt
cxlue   phonxe   soapp   argue

i c a n s p e l l

Use the letters in the book to write six words with the **oa** or **oo** sound on the board.

note
VARIOUS ANSWERS POSSIBLE

9

In the third exercise, your child may have used some of the letters more than once in a word. That's fine, as long as the words that they made are spelled correctly.

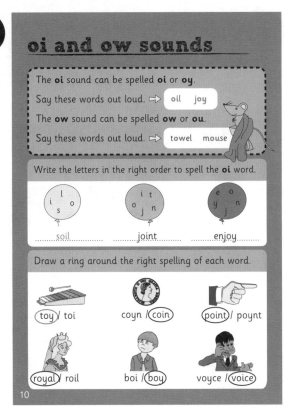

10 — oi and ow sounds

The **oi** sound can be spelled **oi** or **oy**.

Say these words out loud. ⇨ oil joy

The **ow** sound can be spelled **ow** or **ou**.

Say these words out loud. ⇨ towel mouse

Write the letters in the right order to spell the oi word.

s i l o	t o i j n	e o y j n
soil	joint	enjoy

Draw a ring around the right spelling of each word.

(toy) / toi   coyn / (coin)   (point) / poynt

(royal) / roil   boi / (boy)   voyce / (voice)

10

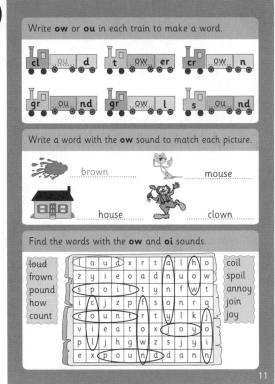

11

Write ow or ou in each train to make a word.

cl **ou** d   t **ow** er   cr **ow** n

gr **ou** nd   gr **ow** l   s **ou** nd

Write a word with the ow sound to match each picture.

brown   mouse

house   clown

Find the words with the ow and oi sounds.

loud
frown
pound
how
count

l	o	u	d	x	r	t	a	l	h	o
z	y	i	e	o	a	d	n	u	o	w
s	p	o	i	l	t	y	n	f	w	t
i	c	j	z	p	f	s	o	n	r	q
c	o	u	n	t	r	t	y	l	k	j
v	i	e	a	t	o	x	j	o	y	o
p	l	j	h	g	w	z	s	j	y	i
e	x	p	o	u	n	d	d	a	n	n

coil
spoil
annoy
join
joy

11

12 — ur, ar and or sounds

The **ur** sound can be spelled **er**, **ir**, **ear** or **ur**.

Say these words out loud. ⇨ her dirt earn nurse

The **ar** sound can be spelled **ar**, **a** or **al**.

Say these words out loud. ⇨ jar father half

Write er, ir or ur to finish the words.

div **er**   p **ur** se   **ear** th

tig **er**   th **ir** d   sk **ir** t

Make six words with the ar sound using these letters.

palm

t a l d f m r

VARIOUS ANSWERS POSSIBLE

12

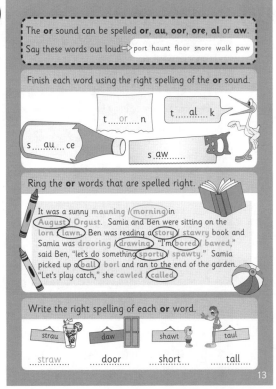

13

The **or** sound can be spelled **or**, **au**, **oor**, **ore**, **al** or **aw**.

Say these words out loud. ⇨ port haunt floor snore walk paw

Finish each word using the right spelling of the or sound.

t **or** n   t **al** k

s **au** ce   s **aw**

Ring the or words that are spelled right.

It was a sunny mauning / (morning) in (August) / Orgust. Samia and Ben were sitting on the lorn / (lawn). Ben was reading a (story) / stawry book and Samia was drooring / (drawing). "I'm (bored) / bawed," said Ben, "let's do something (sporty) / spawty." Samia picked up a (ball) / borl and ran to the end of the garden. "Let's play catch," she cawled / (called).

Write the right spelling of each or word.

strau	daw	shawt	taul
straw	door	short	tall

13

Being able to recognise when a word is spelled incorrectly is a good skill to learn. Encourage your child to check their own writing for any spelling mistakes.

14 — ear and air sounds

The **ear** sound can be spelled **ere**, **ear** or **eer**.

Say these words out loud. ⇨ here fear steer

The **air** sound can be spelled **air**, **ere**, **are** or **ear**.

Say these words out loud. ⇨ fair there dare wear

Colour in the lollies with the right spelling.

heer peer here sphere nere cleer tear appear pere

Use the letters to write six words with the **air** sound.

c	e	i
s	r	n
d	r	a
t	f	w

care ....

VARIOUS ANSWERS POSSIBLE

15

Colour in the words that are spelled right.

| yeer | spair | gear | rare | severe |
| year | spare | gere | rair | seveer |

Cross out one letter from each word so it is spelled right. Write the letter you crossed out in the box to show the secret message.

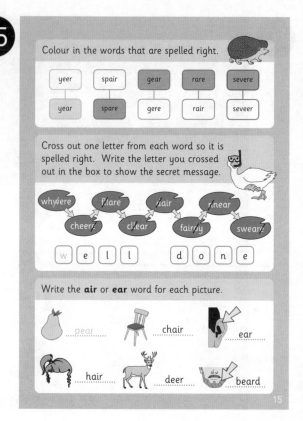

whywere → flare → hair → rnear

cheerz cllear fairoy swearz

w e l l   d o n e

Write the **air** or **ear** word for each picture.

....pear....   ....chair....   ....ear....

....hair....   ....deer....   ....beard....

16 — The ck sound

Quack

The **ck** sound can be spelled **c**, **k**, **ch** or **ck**.

Say these words out loud. ⇨ cat kind chemist block

Choose the right spelling to fill the word puzzle.

1. school / skool
2. cloak / cloack
3. lok / lock
4. kot / cot
5. care / chare
6. kit / cit
7. tik / tick
8. parc / park
9. eko / echo
10. oac / oak

Write a word with the **ck** sound for each picture.

....clock....   ....camel....   ....kick....

....candle....   ....key....   ....anchor....

17 — The f sound

The **f** sound can be spelled **f**, **ff** or **ph**.

Say these words out loud. ⇨ face photo cliff

Draw a ring around the right spelling of each word.

(phone) / fone   dolfin / (dolphin)   (coffee) / cofee

leaff / (leaf)   (snowflake) / snowphlake   girafe / (giraffe)

Write **f**, **ff** or **ph** to finish the words.

to..ff..ee   al..ph..abet   flu..ff..y

..f..rog   gi..f..t   ele..ph..ant

If your child finds any of the words on this page tricky, let them look up the correct spelling in a dictionary. Ask them for the correct spelling later on to check that they remember it.

The sh sound

SHHH

The **sh** sound can be spelled **sh**, **s** or **ci**.

Say these words out loud. ⇨ shape   sure   special

Write the right spelling of each word on the board.

shugar / sugar
pleasure / pleshure
ishue / issue
fresher / frecier
musician / musishan
pressure / preshure

sugar	fresher
pleasure	musician
issue	pressure

Find the words with the **sh** sound.

s	q	o	p	x	z	d	p	d	m	p
h	a	o	u	n	s	u	r	e	o	k
e	f	y	n	s	h	o	e	k	s	v
e	g	j	k	g	j	k	c	w	s	l
p	s	h	e	d	r	d	i	u	i	o
w	r	m	i	a	h	h	o	i	o	p
a	d	e	l	i	c	i	o	u	s	n
d	c	f	r	o	t	i	s	s	u	e

sheep
shed
mission
precious
shoe
unsure
delicious
tissue

Silent letters

Some words have letters in that you write but don't say. These are called silent letters.

Say these words out loud. ⇨ bomb   write   knot

Write the silent letter to finish each of these words.

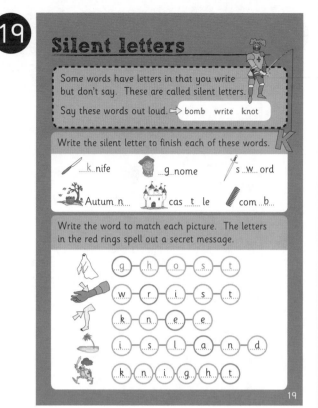

..k.nife   ..g.nome   s ..w.. ord

Autum ..n..   cas ..t.. le   com ..b..

Write the word to match each picture. The letters in the red rings spell out a secret message.

g h o s t
w r i s t
k n e e
i s l a n d
k n i g h t

Double letters

Some words are spelled with double letters but you say them as a single sound.

Say these words out loud. ⇨ tall   mess   fluff

Colour in the words that are spelled right.

kis	wolf	cal	bus	stuff
kiss	wolff	call	buss	stuf

Write the double letters to finish each word.

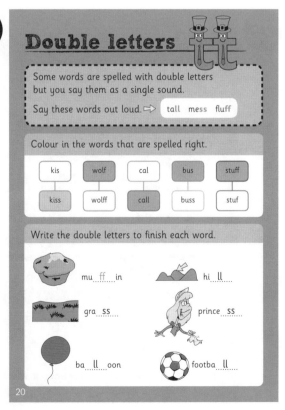

mu ..ff.. in   hi ..ll..

gra ..ss..   prince ..ss..

ba ..ll.. oon   footba ..ll..

Compound words

When two short words are put together to make a longer word it is called a compound word.

For example: tea ✚ spoon ⇨ teaspoon

Draw a ring around the right spelling.

lipstick   hanbag   snoflake   bookmark
lipstik   handbag   snowflake   bookmarke

Fill in the gaps to finish the compound words.

.....wind..... + mill = ...windmill.....

.....star..... + fish = ...starfish.....

.....cow..... + boy = ...cowboy.....

.....straw..... + berry = ...strawberry.....

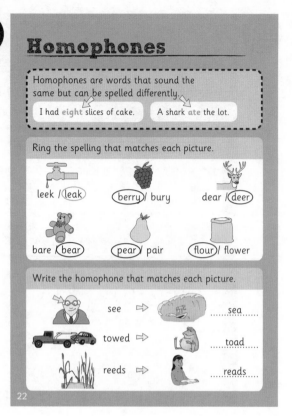

Homophones

Homophones are words that sound the same but can be spelled differently.

I had **eight** slices of cake.   A shark **ate** the lot.

Ring the spelling that matches each picture.

leek / (leak)   (berry) / bury   dear / (deer)

bare / (bear)   (pear) / pair   (flour) / flower

Write the homophone that matches each picture.

see ⟹ ....sea..........

towed ⟹ ....toad..........

reeds ⟹ ....reads..........

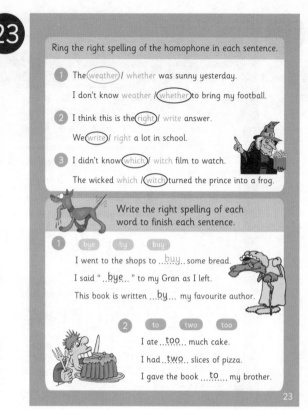

Ring the right spelling of the homophone in each sentence.

1. The (weather) / whether was sunny yesterday.
   I don't know weather / (whether) to bring my football.
2. I think this is the (right) / write answer.
   We (write) / right a lot in school.
3. I didn't know (which) / witch film to watch.
   The wicked which / (witch) turned the prince into a frog.

Write the right spelling of each word to finish each sentence.

1. bye   by   buy
   I went to the shops to ...buy... some bread.
   I said " ..bye.. " to my Gran as I left.
   This book is written ...by... my favourite author.

2. to   two   too
   I ate ..too... much cake.
   I had ..two.. slices of pizza.
   I gave the book ...to... my brother.

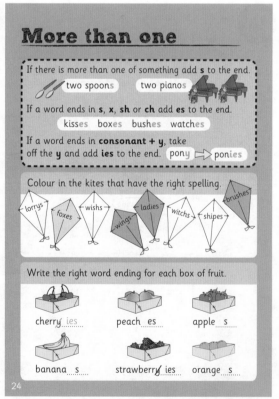

More than one

If there is more than one of something add **s** to the end.
two spoon**s**   two piano**s**

If a word ends in **s**, **x**, **sh** or **ch** add **es** to the end.
kiss**es** box**es** bush**es** watch**es**

If a word ends in **consonant + y**, take off the **y** and add **ies** to the end. pon**y** ⟹ pon**ies**

Colour in the kites that have the right spelling.

lorrys   foxes   wishs   ladies   witchs   wings   shipes   brushes

Write the right word ending for each box of fruit.

cherry _ies_   peach _es_   apple _s_

banana _s_   strawberry _ies_   orange _s_

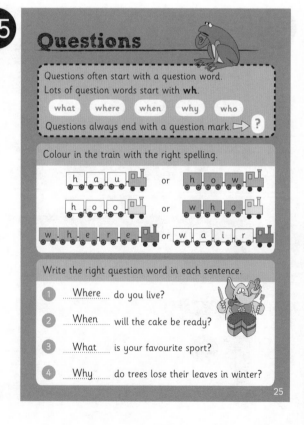

Questions

Questions often start with a question word.
Lots of question words start with **wh**.
what   where   when   why   who
Questions always end with a question mark. ⟹ **?**

Colour in the train with the right spelling.

h a u   or   h o w
h o o   or   w h o
w h e r e   or   w a i r

Write the right question word in each sentence.

1. ....Where.... do you live?
2. ....When.... will the cake be ready?
3. ....What.... is your favourite sport?
4. ....Why.... do trees lose their leaves in winter?

A lot of children find plurals particularly tricky to spell. Remind your child of the rules when they're doing their own writing to give them extra practice.

26 Prefixes

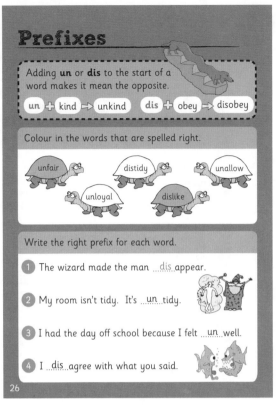

Adding **un** or **dis** to the start of a word makes it mean the opposite.

(un) + kind ➡ unkind (dis) + obey ➡ disobey

Colour in the words that are spelled right.

unfair distidy unallow
unloyal dislike

Write the right prefix for each word.

1 The wizard made the man ...dis.appear.

2 My room isn't tidy. It's ..un..tidy.

3 I had the day off school because I felt ..un.. well.

4 I ..dis..agree with what you said.

26

If your child gets confused about which prefix to use, ask them to say both options out loud and tell you which one sounds right.

27 Suffixes

Adding **ful** or **ly** to the end of a word can make it into a describing word.

help + (ful) ➡ helpful slow + (ly) ➡ slowly

Write the right spelling of each word on the board.

safely / safeful
carely / careful
quickful / quickly
clearly / clearful
useful / usely
costful / costly

safely	clearly
careful	useful
quickly	costly

Add **ly** or **ful** to the words below to make new words.

wonder play pain
love slow wise hope final thought

lovely	wisely	painful
slowly	hopeful	playful
wonderful	finally	thoughtful

27

28 Numbers

Numbers can be written as words. Read these out loud.

4 four 8 eight 12 twelve 15 fifteen

Ring the right spelling of each number.

5 (five) / fyve
2 to / (two)
11 elevin / (eleven)
4 fore / (four)

7 severn / (seven)
18 ateen / (eighteen)
1 won / (one)
20 (twenty) / twentie

Write the word to match each number.

6 six
15 fifteen
thirteen 13
nine 9
8 eight
14 fourteen
twelve 12
three 3

28

29 Days and months

Read these days of the week out loud.

Monday Wednesday Saturday

Read these months out loud.

January April May September

Colour in the days of the week that are spelled right.

Wendesday Teusday Thursday Friday
Monday Sonday Saturday

Write the right spelling of each month.

Joon ➡ June Janury ➡ January
Jewly ➡ July Novemba ➡ November
Aperel ➡ April Disember ➡ December
Mai ➡ May Ocktober ➡ October

29

Encourage your child to write a short diary entry every day. This will give them practice at spelling the names of the days and months.

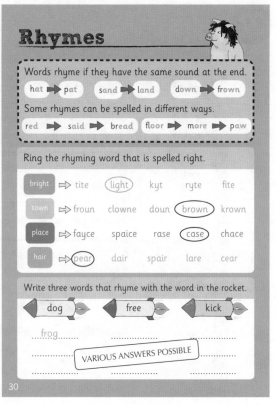

30 Rhymes

Words rhyme if they have the same sound at the end.

hat ➡ pat   sand ➡ land   down ➡ frown

Some rhymes can be spelled in different ways.

red ➡ said ➡ bread   floor ➡ more ➡ paw

Ring the rhyming word that is spelled right.

bright ➡ tite   (light)   kyt   ryte   fite

town ➡ froun   clowne   doun   (brown)   krown

place ➡ fayce   spaice   rase   (case)   chace

hair ➡ (pear)   dair   spair   lare   cear

Write three words that rhyme with the word in the rocket.

◀ dog   ◀ free   ◀ kick

frog ....
.... VARIOUS ANSWERS POSSIBLE ....
....

30

Make sure your child understands that rhyming words don't always have the same spelling pattern.

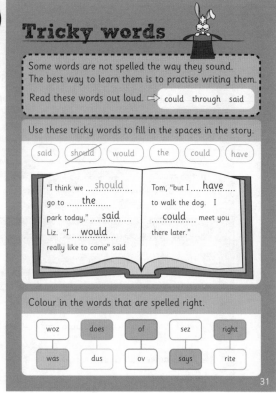

31 Tricky words

Some words are not spelled the way they sound. The best way to learn them is to practise writing them.

Read these words out loud. ➡ could   through   said

Use these tricky words to fill in the spaces in the story.

said   (should)   would   the   could   have

"I think we should go to the park today," said Liz. "I would really like to come" said

Tom, "but I have to walk the dog. I could meet you there later."

Colour in the words that are spelled right.

| woz | does | of | sez | right |
| was | dus | ov | says | rite |

31

32 Handy spelling hints

Break words into smaller bits to help you spell them.

however ➡ how ev er   donkey ➡ don key

Break these long words into smaller bits.

choc   .o.   late
ball   oon
oct   .o.   pus

Make up sentences to help you spell tricky words.

because ➡ big elephants can actually understand small elephants

Make up sentences to help you spell these words.

said   silly ants inspect dragons
does   ....
who   VARIOUS ANSWERS POSSIBLE ....

32

Help your child make up sentences to spell any words that they find tricky. The funnier the sentence, the easier they'll find it to remember.

Race to the Spell Book

You'll need a counter for each player and a dice. Place your counters at the start, and take it in turns to roll the dice once. Follow the instructions when you land on them.

start   cloud   purse   knife   pear   anchor   ghost   Wednesday   finish

Possible answers include: strawberry, goldfish, hairbrush.

The f sound

The **f** sound can be spelled **f**, **ff** or **ph**.

Say these words out loud. ⟹ face   cliff   **ph**oto

Draw a ring around the right spelling of each word.

(phone) / fone

dolfin / dolphin

coffee / cofee

leaff / leaf

snowflake / snowphlake

girafe / giraffe

Write **f**, **ff** or **ph** to finish the words.

to ..ff.. ee

al.......abet

flu.......y

.........rog

gi.......t

ele.......ant

17

The sh sound

SHHH

The **sh** sound can be spelled **sh**, **s** or **ci**.

Say these words out loud. ⟹ **sh**ape **s**ure spe**ci**al

Write the right spelling of each word on the board.

shugar / sugar
pleasure / pleshure
ishue / issue
fresher / frecier
musician / musishan
pressure / preshure

..........sugar.......... ....

....

....

Find the words with the **sh** sound.

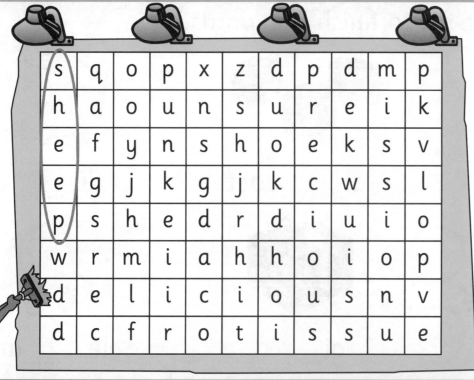

s	q	o	p	x	z	d	p	d	m	p
h	a	o	u	n	s	u	r	e	i	k
e	e	f	y	n	s	h	o	e	k	s	v
e	g	j	k	g	j	k	c	w	s	l
p	s	h	e	d	r	d	i	u	i	o
w	r	m	i	a	h	h	o	i	o	p
d	e	l	i	c	i	o	u	s	n	v
d	c	f	r	o	t	i	s	s	u	e

sheep
shed
mission
precious
shoe
unsure
delicious
tissue

18

Silent letters

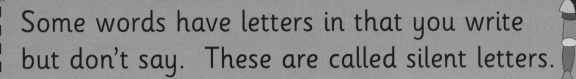

Some words have letters in that you write but don't say. These are called silent letters.

Say these words out loud. ⟹ bom**b**   **w**rite   **k**not

Write the silent letter to finish each of these words.

 ...k..nife

  ....nome

  s .... ord

  Autum........

  cas .... le

 com ....

Write the word to match each picture. The letters in the red rings spell out a secret message.

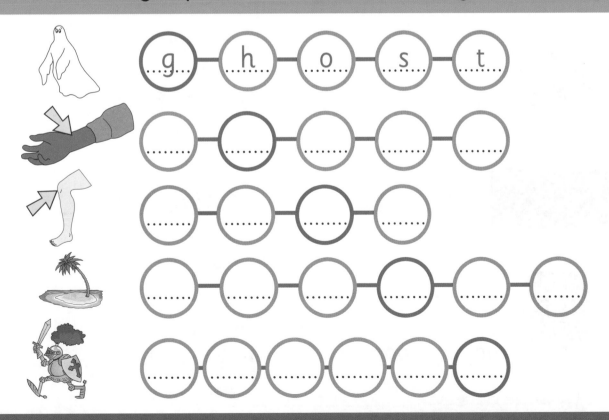

Double letters

Some words are spelled with double letters but you say them as a single sound.

Say these words out loud. ⇨ **tall mess fluff**

Colour in the words that are spelled right.

kis	wolf	cal	bus	stuff
kiss	wolff	call	buss	stuf

Write the double letters to finish each word.

 mu...ff...in

 hi..........

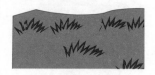 gra..........

 prince..........

 ba..........oon

 footba..........

Compound words

When two short words are put together to make a longer word it is called a compound word.

For example: tea + spoon ⟹ teaspoon

Draw a ring around the right spelling.

(lipstick)
lipstik

hanbag
handbag

snoflake
snowflake

bookmark
bookmarke

Fill in the gaps to finish the compound words.

............wind............ + mill = ...windmill............

.... + fish = ...

.... + boy = ...

.... + berry = ...

Homophones

Homophones are words that sound the same but can be spelled differently.

I had **eight** slices of cake.

A shark **ate** the lot.

Ring the spelling that matches each picture.

 leek / (leak)

 berry / bury

 dear / deer

 bare / bear

 pear / pair

 flour / flower

Write the homophone that matches each picture.

 see ⟹  ....

 towed ⟹ ....

 reeds ⟹ ....

Ring the right spelling of the homophone in each sentence.

1 The (weather) / whether was sunny yesterday.

I don't know weather / whether to bring my football.

2 I think this is the right / write answer.

We write / right a lot in school.

3 I didn't know which / witch film to watch.

The wicked which / witch turned the prince into a frog.

Write the right spelling of each word to finish each sentence.

1 bye   by   buy

I went to the shops to ....buy.. some bread.

I said " .... " to my Gran as I left.

This book is written .... my favourite author.

2 to   two   too

I ate .... much cake.

I had .... slices of pizza.

I gave the book .... my brother.

23

More than one

If there is more than one of something add **s** to the end.

 two spoon**s**   two piano**s**

If a word ends in **s**, **x**, **sh** or **ch** add **es** to the end.

kiss**es**   box**es**   bush**es**   watch**es**

If a word ends in **consonant + y**, take
off the **y** and add **ies** to the end.   pon**y** ⇨ pon**ies**

Colour in the kites that have the right spelling.

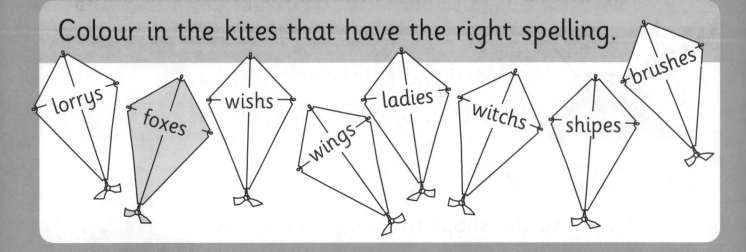

lorrys   foxes   wishs   wings   ladies   witchs   shipes   brushes

Write the right word ending for each box of fruit.

cherr~~y~~ ies

peach..........

apple..........

banana..........

strawberry..........

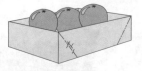

orange..........

Questions

Questions often start with a question word.
Lots of question words start with **wh**.

what   where   when   why   who

Questions always end with a question mark. ⇒ ?

Colour in the train with the right spelling.

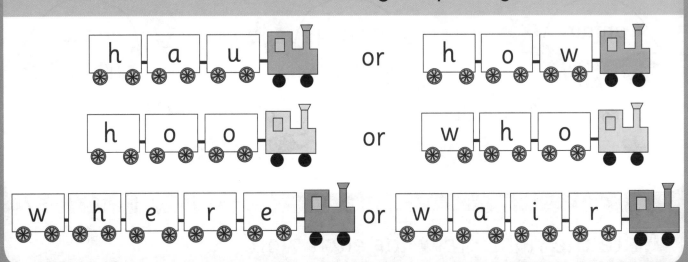

h a u   or   h o w

h o o   or   w h o

w h e r e   or   w a i r

Write the right question word in each sentence.

1 .... do you live?

2 .... will the cake be ready?

3 .... is your favourite sport?

4 .... do trees lose their leaves in winter?

Prefixes

Adding **un** or **dis** to the start of a word makes it mean the opposite.

un + kind ➡ unkind   dis + obey ➡ disobey

Colour in the words that are spelled right.

unfair   distidy   unallow

unloyal   dislike

Write the right prefix for each word.

1 The wizard made the man ....dis.. appear.

2 My room isn't tidy. It's ....tidy.

3 I had the day off school because I felt ....well.

4 I ....agree with what you said.

26

Suffixes

Adding **ful** or **ly** to the end of a word can make it into a describing word.

help ➕ **ful** ➡ helpful   slow ➕ **ly** ➡ slowly

Word Glue

Write the right spelling of each word on the board.

safely / safeful

carely / careful

quickful / quickly

clearly / clearful

useful / usely

costful / costly

...........safely...........   ....

....

....

Add **ly** or **ful** to the words below to make new words.

love   ful   slow   wonder   wise   hope   play   pain   final   ly   thought

...........lovely...........   ....

....

....

Numbers

Ring the right spelling of each number.

5
(five) / fyve

2
to / two

11
elevin / eleven

4
fore / four

7
severn / seven

18
ateen / eighteen

1
won / one

20
twenty / twentie

Write the word to match each number.

6 six ....

15 ....

.... 13

.... 9

8 ....

14 ....

.... 12

.... 3

28

Days and months

Read these days of the week out loud.

Monday   **Wednesday**   **Saturday**

Read these months out loud.

January   **April**   **May**   **September**

Colour in the days of the week that are spelled right.

Wendesday   Teusday   Thursday   Friday

Monday   Sonday   Saturday

Write the right spelling of each month.

 ⇒ June

Janury ⇒ ....

Jewly ⇒ ....

Novemba ⇒ ....

Aperel ⇒ ....

Disember ⇒ ....

Mai ⇒ ....

Ocktober ⇒ ....

Rhymes

Words rhyme if they have the same sound at the end.

hat pat   sand → land   down → frown

Some rhymes can be spelled in different ways.

red → said → bread   floor → more → paw

Ring the rhyming word that is spelled right.

bright	tite	(light)	kyt	ryte	fite
town ⇒	froun	clowne	doun	brown	krown
place ⇒	fayce	spaice	rase	case	chace
hair ⇒	pear	dair	spair	lare	cear

Write three words that rhyme with the word in the rocket.

 dog   free   kick

frog ....

....

....

....

....

....

....

....

....

Tricky words

Some words are not spelled the way they sound. The best way to learn them is to practise writing them.

Read these words out loud. ⇨ could   through   said

Use these tricky words to fill in the spaces in the story.

(said)   (~~should~~)   (would)   (the)   (could)   (have)

"I think we ......should...... go to .... park today," .... Liz. "I .... really like to come" said

Tom, "but I .... to walk the dog.   I .... meet you there later."

Colour in the words that are spelled right.

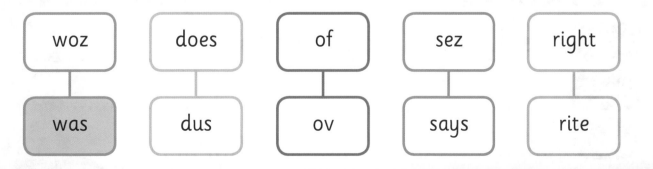

| woz | does | of | sez | right |
| was | dus | ov | says | rite |

31

Handy spelling hints

Break words into smaller bits to help you spell them.

Break these long words into smaller bits.

choc	...o...	..late..

Make up sentences to help you spell tricky words.

because ⇒ **b**ig **e**lephants **c**an **a**ctually **u**nderstand **s**mall **e**lephants

Make up sentences to help you spell these words.

said   **s**illy **a**nts **i**nspect **d**ragons ....

does   ....

who   ....

32